THE BEST OF

DILBERT™

VOLUME 2

Selected cartoons from ALWAYS POSTPONE MEETINGS
WITH TIME-WASTING MORONS by Scott Adams

SCOTT ADAMS

B■XTREE

First published 2002 by Boxtree
an imprint of Pan Macmillan Ltd
Pan Macmillan, 20 New Wharf Road, London N1 9RR
Basingstoke and Oxford
Associated companies throughout the world
www.panmacmillan.com

ISBN 0 7522 15000

1 3 5 7 9 8 6 4 2

A CIP catalogue record for this book is available from the British Library.

Printed and bound in Great Britain by
Mackays of Chatham plc, Chatham, Kent

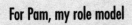
For Pam, my role model

INTRODUCTION

Thank you for buying this book. My editor asked me to write an introduction and here it is. I don't have anything to say, but frankly, I doubt anybody will read the introduction anyway; unless you're on a long plane ride and you've already read everything else including the barf bag instructions, and you're looking desperately for something you haven't read - something to take your mind off the fact that most commercial aircraft fleets are well beyond their intended technological life, and the chances are very good that you will soon be engulfed in flames, racing toward the ground at Math One while cursing yourself for not listening to the pre-flight safety instructions. No you had to be nonchalant and conspicuously ignore the flight attendant, like you're some kind of big-time traveller or something. And now, because of your ego, they'll be sifting the wreckage for enough of your bony matter to fill an envelope with your name on it. And the guy sitting next to you will be interviewed on CNN saying how he watched you being devoured by flames from the comfort of his emergency asbestos suit which he knew how to get into because he paid attention to the flight attendant. But I digress.

The point is that I have to write this introduction. I'm almost done, I think it's going pretty well so far. Okay, I'm done.

I'VE DECIDED TO DEDICATE MY LIFE TO THE LESS FORTUNATE.

THAT'S VERY NOBLE OF YOU, DOGBERT. WILL YOU BE WORKING WITH THE HOMELESS, OR PERHAPS THE HUNGRY?

© 1989 United Feature Syndicate, Inc.

4-18

S. Adams

I THOUGHT I'D START WITH PEOPLE WHO DIDN'T BUY REAL ESTATE IN THE 70's ... MAYBE WORK MY WAY UP TO THAT OTHER STUFF.

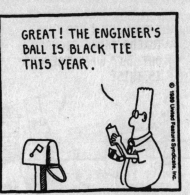

GREAT! THE ENGINEER'S BALL IS BLACK TIE THIS YEAR.

© 1989 United Feature Syndicate, Inc.

I WILL BE RENTING A TUXEDO FOR THE BALL, AND I WOULD LIKE IT IF YOU COULD KEEP ANY SNIDE COMMENTS TO YOURSELF.

GOSH. EVEN I WOULDN'T MAKE FUN OF A GUY WHO WOULD PAY SIXTY-FIVE BUCKS TO WEAR BORROWED PANTS.

4-24 S. Adams

15

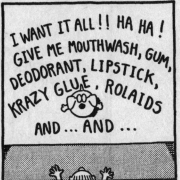

© 1989 United Feature Syndicate, Inc.

17

I'VE DECIDED TO MAKE SOME DOG FRIENDS, BUT I DON'T EVEN KNOW WHAT OTHER DOGS DO WHEN THEY GET TOGETHER.

WELL, I SUPPOSE THEY WOULD BARK LIKE IDIOTS, RUN AROUND IN CIRCLES, AND SNIFF EVERY PART OF YOUR BODY.

I GUESS "SCRABBLE" IS OUT OF THE QUESTION.

J. Adams 5-16

IMAGINE MY SURPRISE WHEN I SAW THIS AD FOR DOCTOR DOGBERT'S SEMINAR ON DEVELOPING SELF-CONFIDENCE. OKAY, WHAT'S THE SCAM?

I FIGURED THIS WOULD BE A GOOD WAY TO FIND A BUNCH OF MEEK PEOPLE TO DO MY BIDDING. IF THEY REFUSE, I'LL YELL AT THEM AND HURT THEIR LITTLE FEELINGS.

5-22

S. Adams

THEN I'LL LEVERAGE THAT POWER INTO VAST WEALTH OR MAYBE WORLD DOMINATION.

NO! BAD DOGGY!

© 1989 United Feature Syndicate, Inc.

WHY DO YOU WASTE YOUR TIME READING BOOKS?

BECAUSE READING INCREASES MY KNOWLEDGE, AND KNOWLEDGE IS POWER.

BUT POWER CORRUPTS...

...AND CORRUPTION IS A CRIME...

AND CRIME DOESN'T PAY...

IF YOU KEEP READING, YOU'LL GO BROKE!!!

5-28

GOSH! IT ALWAYS SEEMED SO...SO ...HARMLESS.

OH YEAH, THE LIBRARIANS WOULD LOVE TO HAVE YOU BELIEVE THAT!

S. Adams 6-11

48

"SINGLE, DUMPY AND DULL MALE SEEKS YOUNG AND BEAUTIFUL WOMAN FOR ROMANCE."

THE KEY TO WRITING A SUCCESSFUL "PERSONALS" AD IS HONESTY... COMPLETE AND TOTAL HONESTY.

6-21

WHAT SPECIES ARE YOU TARGETING?

S.Adams

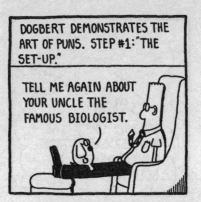

DOGBERT DEMONSTRATES THE ART OF PUNS. STEP #1: "THE SET-UP."

TELL ME AGAIN ABOUT YOUR UNCLE THE FAMOUS BIOLOGIST.

UNCLE ALBERT WON MANY AWARDS FOR HIS WORK IN BREEDING SEA ANEMONES.

SADLY, HE HAD LITTLE TIME FOR A SOCIAL LIFE.

6-24

STEP #2: "THE DELIVERY" (FROM OUTSIDE OF SWATTING RANGE).

WITH ANEMONES LIKE THAT, WHO NEEDS FRIENDS?

DING
DONG

I'LL GET THE DOOR.

GREETINGS, EARTHLING. WE ARE AN ADVANCED RACE FROM THE PLANET MOOTHRON.

WE CAME TO SHARE OUR SECRETS FOR ENDING HUNGER, POVERTY AND DISEASE.

WHAT'S IN IT FOR ME?

© 1989 United Feature Syndicate, Inc.

I'LL ALWAYS WONDER IF THERE WAS A BETTER WAY TO HANDLE THAT.

S. Adams 7-9

...AND NATURE HAS A WAY OF COMPENSATING FOR WEAKNESSES.

REALLY?

THAT'S WHY BLIND PEOPLE OFTEN DEVELOP GREAT HEARING.

S. Adams

I GUESS THAT ALSO EXPLAINS WHY STUPID PEOPLE HAVE BIG MOUTHS.

© 1989 United Feature Syndicate, Inc.

7-10

HOW TO BE BORING: "GREAT THINGS I HAVE EATEN" SERIES.

BUT BY FAR, THE BEST BAKED POTATO I'VE EVER EATEN WAS SIX YEARS AGO...

THE VICTIM MAY TRY SARCASM TO RELIEVE THE BOREDOM.

FASCINATING. NOW COULD YOU THINK OUT LOUD ALL OF THE POSSIBLE DATES THIS MAY HAVE OCCURRED?

© 1989 United Feature Syndicate, Inc.

S. Adams

SARCASM WON'T WORK.

WELL, IT COULD HAVE BEEN ON OCTOBER 6TH... OR MAYBE THE 16TH. WAS THAT A TUESDAY?

7-14

THIS DESIGN COULD CHANGE THE WAY THE WORLD BARBECUES. NO MORE STRUGGLING WITH CHARCOAL.

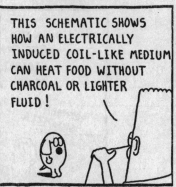

THIS SCHEMATIC SHOWS HOW AN ELECTRICALLY INDUCED COIL-LIKE MEDIUM CAN HEAT FOOD WITHOUT CHARCOAL OR LIGHTER FLUID!

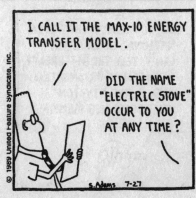

I CALL IT THE MAX-10 ENERGY TRANSFER MODEL.

DID THE NAME "ELECTRIC STOVE" OCCUR TO YOU AT ANY TIME?

S. Adams 7-27

ONE MORE ADJUSTMENT AND MY TRANS-DIMENSIONAL RADIO WILL BE COMPLETE.

PHZEEM

WUMP! WUMP!

© 1989 United Feature Syndicate, Inc.

WELCOME TO THE LAND OF OVERUSED PHRASES.

BOY, THEY LET ANYBODY IN HERE.

UH... HI, HOW ARE YOU?

NOT BAD FOR A WEDNESDAY!

LET ME GIVE YOU THE TEN-CENT TOUR.

OUCH! I'LL JUST WALK ON THE BOTTOMS.

YOU KNOW, SWIMMING IS THE BEST FORM OF EXERCISE.

THE CHOSEN ONE!!!

NAH. I'M JUST PULLING YOUR LEGS.

8-6 S.Adams

87

YOU'VE BEEN READING THAT WORLD ALMANAC FOR HOURS.

I'M LOOKING FOR NATIONS I CAN CONQUER ON A LIMITED BUDGET.

HERE'S ONE: "ANDORRA. 185 SQUARE MILES. ONLY 56,000 PEOPLE. JOINT RULE BY FRANCE AND SPAIN..."

HMM..."KING DOGBERT OF ANDORRA" HAS A NICE RING TO IT. NOW I JUST NEED SOME MERCENARIES.

HOW ARE YOU GOING TO PAY FOR MERCENARIES?

I'LL FLOAT SOME JUNK BONDS UNTIL WE CAN LOOT THE TREASURY OF ANDORRA.

© 1989 United Feature Syndicate, Inc.

IT STRIKES ME AS A BIT UNETHICAL.

APPARENTLY I'LL HAVE TO IMPRISON SOME DISSIDENTS.

9/10

S. Adams

TO HIS HORROR, DILBERT DISCOVERS THAT ALL OF HIS WHITE SOCKS HAVE HOLES. "MY GOODNESS!" HE CRIES, "I SHALL BE FORCED TO WEAR BLACK SOCKS TO WORK!"

S. Adams

"IF ONLY MY PANTS REACHED THE TOPS OF MY SHOES, THEN THE OTHER ENGINEERS MIGHT NOT NOTICE," DILBERT DESPAIRED.

CLICK CLICK

WHAT ARE YOU WRITING?

9-13

IT'S A "GEEK" TRAGEDY.

WOW! AND I THOUGHT THIS WAS JUST MORE JUNK MAIL!

ALL I HAVE TO DO IS DRIVE TWO HOURS AND LISTEN TO THEIR CONDO SALES PITCH. I'M <u>GUARANTEED</u> TO WIN A JEEP CHEROKEE OR A VALUABLE MOCK EMERALD.

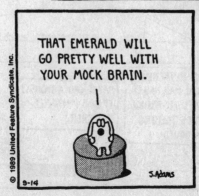

THAT EMERALD WILL GO PRETTY WELL WITH YOUR MOCK BRAIN.

9-14

S.Adams

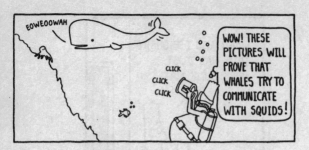

MY NEW SECURITY SYSTEM IS NOW INSTALLED.

TAP TAP

HOW'S IT WORK?

I BURIED A GIANT SPRING UNDER THE WELCOME MAT TO CATAPULT ANY UNDESIRABLES INTO THE WILSEY'S POOL THREE BLOCKS FROM HERE.

YOU JUST TAP THAT LITTLE BUTTON ON THE FLOOR THERE...

TIME STANDS STILL AS DOGBERT PONDERS THE GIFT THAT FATE HAS GIVEN HIM.

I'M PRETTY SURE THE LOOK ON HIS FACE WILL BE WORTH WHATEVER MINOR GUILT I FEEL OVER THIS.

10-8

DILBERT DEMONSTRATES THE ART OF JOKE TELLING.

...SO THE FIRST GUY ORDERS A BEER AND A CACTUS...

S.Adams

A GOOD JOKE TELLER WILL SEEK TO ESTABLISH A PATTERN.

...THEN THE SECOND GUY...HEH, HEH...ORDERS A BEER AND A CACTUS...

8-5

TOMORROW'S LESSON: TIMING.

...SO THEN THE SEVENTY-THIRD GUY COMES IN...

ZZZZZZz

A FRIEND IS SOMEBODY WHO WILL NOT THINK LESS OF YOU FOR SINGING THE "OOH-OOH!" PART OF A SONG ON THE RADIO.

OF COURSE, FRIENDS WILL ALSO FEEL FREE TO EXPRESS THEIR MUSICAL OPINIONS.

...BUT I WASN'T ALWAYS A CONSERVATIVE ENGINEER-TYPE.

I WAS QUITE THE LITTLE REBEL WHEN I WAS A KID.

© 1989 United Feature Syndicate, Inc.

FLASHBACK

POTATO SALAD AGAIN? I'VE <u>GOT</u> TO SPEAK OUT ON THIS ISSUE.

S. Adams

9-29